STOP!

EACH GOOD VS EVIL BOOK HAS TWO STORIES –
ONE BLUE AND ONE RED – BUT YOU CAN READ
IT IN MANY DIFFERENT WAYS . . .

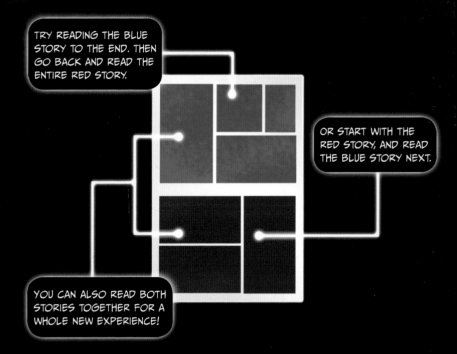

TRY READING THE BLUE
STORY TO THE END. THEN
GO BACK AND READ THE
ENTIRE RED STORY.

OR START WITH THE
RED STORY, AND READ
THE BLUE STORY NEXT.

YOU CAN ALSO READ BOTH
STORIES TOGETHER FOR A
WHOLE NEW EXPERIENCE!

IT'S UP TO YOU!

READ THIS BOOK AGAIN AND AGAIN TO DISCOVER EXCITING
NEW DETAILS IN THE NEVER-ENDING BATTLE OF . . . GOOD VS EVIL.

GOOD vs EVIL

Adventure

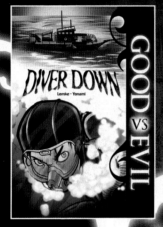

Fantasy

Science Fiction

Horror

COLLECT THEM ALL!

GOOD vs EVIL

DIVER DOWN

by
Donald Lemke

illustrated by
Yonami

www.raintreepublishers.co.uk
Visit our website to find out
more information about
Raintree books.

To order:
☎ Phone 0845 6044371
🖷 Fax +44 (0) 1865 312263
🖻 Email myorders@raintreepublishers.co.uk

Customers from outside the UK please telephone +44 1865 312262

Raintree is an imprint of Capstone Global Library Limited,
a company incorporated in England and Wales having its registered office at
7 Pilgrim Street, London, EC4V 6LB
– Registered company number: 6695582

Copyright © 2012 by Stone Arch Books
First published in the United Kingdom
in paperback in 2012
The moral rights of the proprietor have been asserted.

Story by Donald Lemke
Illustrated by Yonami
Colour by Glass House Graphics
Series Designer: Brann Garvey
Series Editor: Donald Lemke
Editorial Director: Michael Dahl
Art Director: Bob Lentz
Creative Director: Heather Kindseth
Originated by Capstone Global Library Ltd
Printed and bound in China by Leo Paper Products Ltd

ISBN 978 1 406 24322 2 (paperback)
16 15 14 13 12
10 9 8 7 6 5 4 3 2 1

British Library Cataloguing in Publication Data
A full catalogue record for this book is available
from the British Library.

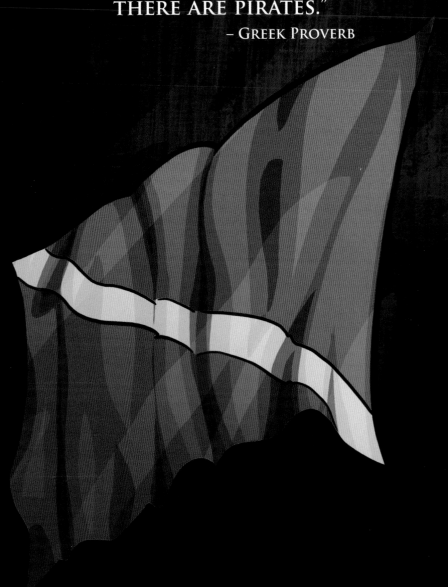

"WHERE THERE IS A SEA,
THERE ARE PIRATES."

– GREEK PROVERB

ABOVE THE WAVES

ON A CLOUDLESS DAY, THE CREW OF AN AMERICAN DIVE BOAT SEARCHES THE PACIFIC OCEAN FOR THE REMAINS OF A SUNKEN SUBMARINE AND ITS MYSTERIOUS CARGO . . .

GOOD VS EVIL

BENEATH THE SEA

FAR BENEATH THE CLEAR BLUE SEA, A DIVE TEAM RACES AGAINST TIME TO FIND THE TREASURE FROM A SUNKEN SUBMARINE. THEY'LL STOP AT NOTHING TO CAPTURE THE CARGO FIRST AND KEEP THE SUNKEN SUB A SECRET . . .

GET THE CARGO AND GET BACK UP.

THESE WATERS AREN'T EXACTLY FRIENDLY.

8

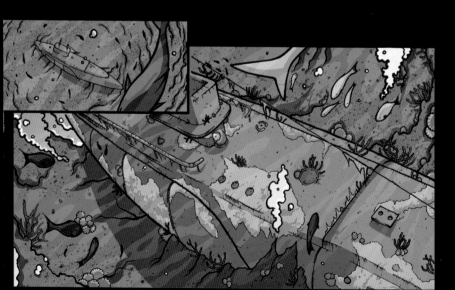

YOU GOT IT, BOSS!

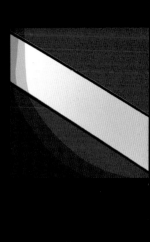

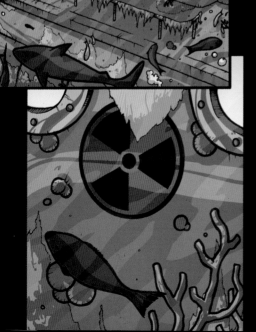

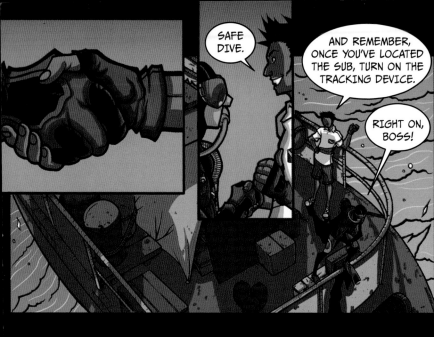

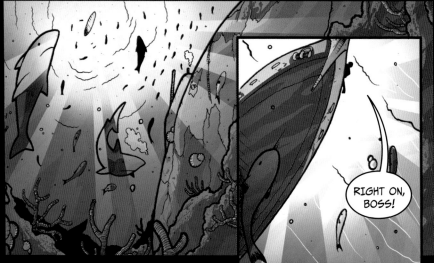

SPLASH!

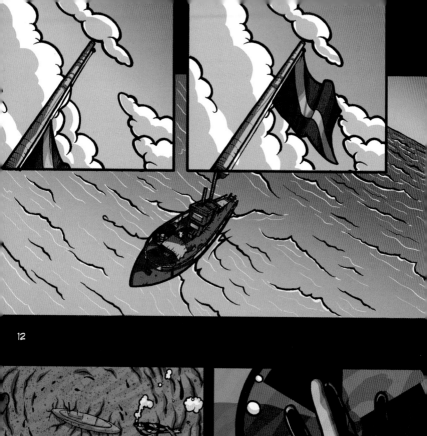

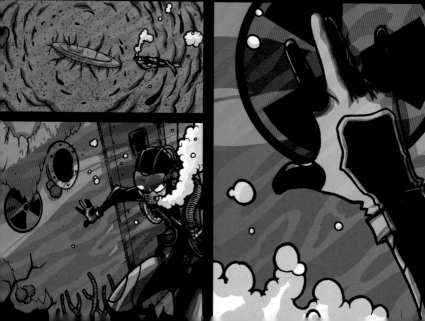

14

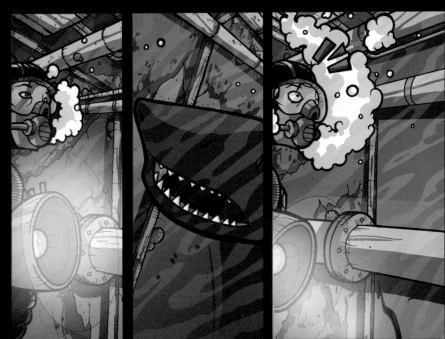

I HAVE TO DO SOMETHING.

16

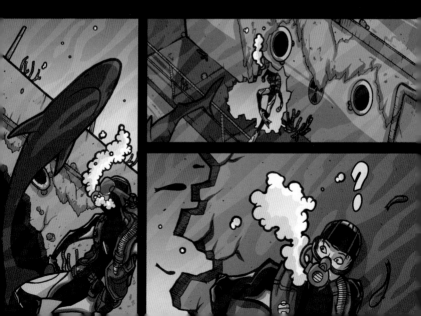

KNOCK, KNOCK.
IS ANYONE
HOME?

BWOOP!

BWOOP!

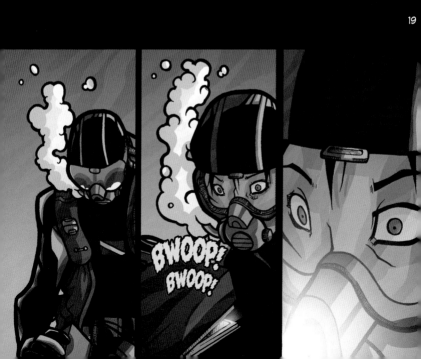

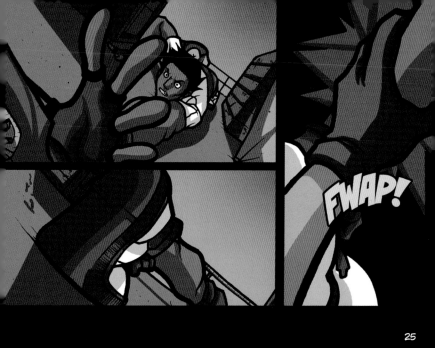

FWAP!

FWAP!

JUST HOLD STILL.

SCHING!

YOU MIGHT
WANT TO CLOSE
YOUR EYES.

33

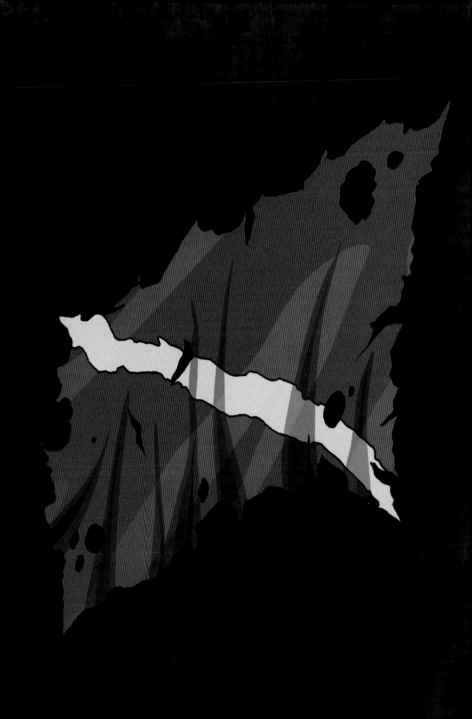

SCRIPT BY

Donald Lemke works as a children's book editor and writer in Minneapolis, USA. He is the author of the Zinc Alloy graphic novel adventure series. He also wrote *Captured Off Guard*, a World War II story, and a graphic novelization of *Gulliver's Travels*, both of which were selected by the Junior Library Guild in the United States. Most recently, Lemke has written several DC Comics chapter books.

VISUAL GLOSSARY

SCUBA FLAG

In the United States, Canada, and several other countries, boats must fly a scuba or "Diver Down" flag to indicate a diver is under the water.

ALPHA FLAG

Throughout Europe, and much of the world, dive boats fly the Alpha, or Alfa signal flag, which means, "I have a diver down; keep well clear at slow speed."

RADIATION SIGN

Hazard symbols warn people of toxic chemicals. A radiation sign, like the one seen on the sunken submarine, indicates the presence of radiation, potentially toxic emissions from nuclear decay.

STAR BURSTS

In comics or manga, illustrators sometimes use star bursts to draw attention to the most important object in a panel, such as a knife in someone's hand.

FACIAL EXPRESSIONS

Illustrators often indicate emotions, such as happiness, fear, or surprise, by exaggerating facial expressions of their characters. Wide eyes, a furrowed brow, or an open mouth can outwardly show a person's inner feelings.

VISUAL QUESTIONS

1. Throughout the story, "action lines" or "lines of force" are displayed above a character's head. What do you believe is the purpose of these lines?

2. The way a character's eyes and mouth look, also known as their facial expression, can tell you a lot about the emotions he or she is feeling. In the image to the left, how do you think the character is feeling? Use the illustration to explain your answer.

3. A person's physical gestures, poses, and expressions can sometimes indicate whether they are good or evil. Looking at the characters below, which do you think is good? Which is evil? Why?

4. Like these panels from page 25, the top and bottom images are often similar. Why do you think the illustrator shows these two things happening at the same time? Can you find other instances?

5. On page 29, one of the boat captains pierces a tank of liquid with his knife. The tank isn't labelled, but what do you believe was inside? What clues led you to this conclusion?

6. On page 36, the top and bottom stories merge, and the diver is shown above and below the sea. What do the images tell you about the diver's chances? Do you think he'll survive? Explain.

CREATING THE BOOK

THE MANUSCRIPT

Graphic novels are often created by two different people – a writer and an illustrator. Even when a book contains few words, the writer must provide detailed notes called "scene descriptions", instructing the content of each panel.

A page from the *Diver Down* manuscript:

PAGE 23

Panel 1
Long shot of Enemy Crewman running into the foreground. Motion lines emanate from his body to show speed.

Panel 2
Wide shot of Enemy Crewman jumping from the deck of the enemy dive boat towards the US dive boat. The US Crewman stands on the US dive boat's deck, dropping the harpoon gun and shielding himself against the coming impact.

Panel 3
Medium shot of Enemy Crewman tackling the US Crewman onto the deck of the US dive boat.

Panel 4
Close-up shot of Enemy Diver's white-gloved fist striking the US Diver's scuba mask.

Panel 5
Close-up shot of US Diver grabbing the Enemy Diver's hand.

Panel 6
Close-up shot of US Diver using his other black-gloved fist to strike the Enemy Diver's scuba mask. (PLEASE NOTE: On the Enemy Diver's all-white wet suit, there's an Alpha Flag on the chest.)

PENCILS

After receiving the manuscript from the writer, the illustrator creates rough sketches called "pencils". The writer and editor of the book review these drawings, making sure all corrections are made before continuing to the next stage.

From page 23 of *Diver Down*:

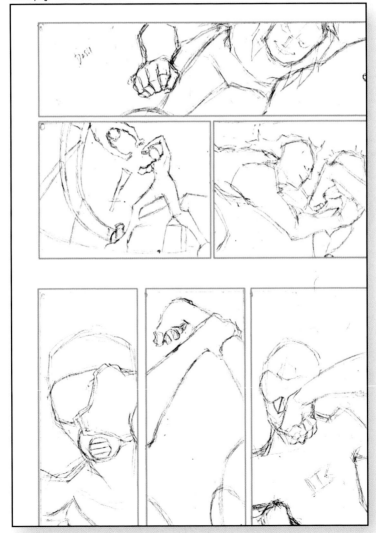

INKS

When illustrations have been approved by the editor, an artist, sometimes called an "inker", draws over the pencils in ink. This stage allows readers to see the illustration more easily in print.

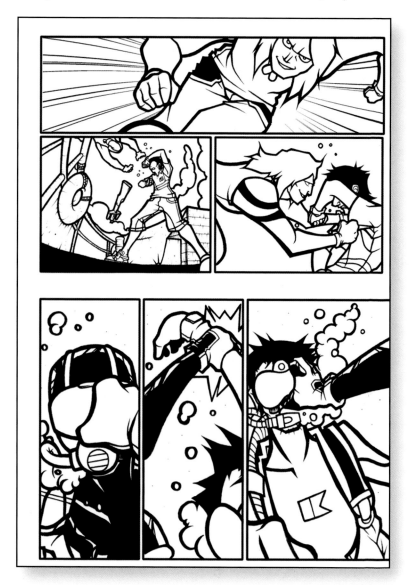

COLOURS

Next, the inks are sent to a "colourist" who adds colour to each panel of art.

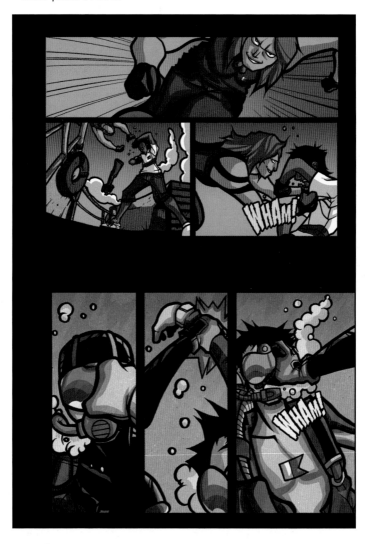

When the art is completed, designers add the final touches, including speech bubbles and sound effects. Turn to page 23 to see the final version.